Learning Resource Centre
To renew this item,
telephone **01925 494422**

Warrington Collegiate

**This book is to be returned to the Learning Resource Centre
on or before the last date stamped below.**

Illustrated by Stephen Elford

With special thanks to our reader:
Vincent Baker

First published in 2009 in Great Britain by
Barrington Stoke Ltd
18 Walker St, Edinburgh, EH3 7LP

www.barringtonstoke.co.uk

Title ISBN: 978-1-84299-702-4
Pack ISBN: 978-84299-788-8

Printed in Great Britain by The Charlesworth Group

Dead Man File

Name: Luke Smith

Age: 16

Cause of death: Car crash. Serious head and back injuries.

Date of case 3: September 2009

Mission: To save my girlfriend from danger.

Cont

Intro

Luke Smith was killed in a car driven by his best mate, Joe. But that was not the end of it. Luke comes back as a ghost. What can he do to help people now he is dead?

Name:
Luke Smith
Age:
16

Chapter 1

I'm Luke Smith and I'm dead. Yasmin was my girl until the crash. She was stunning. All the boys liked her. She went to bits when I died.

She didn't know that I was still around, watching her. How could she know that I was a ghost? Ghosts are hardly ever seen.

Yasmin, with Ann and Jenny, went to discos and clubs. I wasn't happy for her. There had been some bad things in town. Five girls had gone missing in three weeks. Where were they? Alive or dead?

Name:
Luke Smith
Age:
16

Chapter 2

On Saturday I went after them to Jet Set. It was THE best club in town. It was always very full. Jenny got the drinks and then the three girls had a dance.

A man drifted across the room. He was
wearing sun glasses and a black hat. He
looked at the three girls. He took some
white stuff out of his pocket and dropped it
into two of the girls' drinks. He was a
spiker.

Name:
Luke Smith
Age:
I6

Chapter 3

What could I do? Yasmin was OK
because he missed out her drink. But soon
Ann and Jenny were nearly asleep. Yasmin
helped them out of the club.

"You two must be ill," Yasmin said.

The man in the sun glasses came out after them. "Hi. Your friends look ill. Can I help you take them home?"

"Thanks," said Yasmin.

Name:
Luke Smith
Age:
16

Chapter 4

After a short walk, the girls could hardly stand.

"I live here," said the man in the sun glasses, "they can rest on my sofa."

When we were inside his house he mixed drinks for himself and Yasmin. They left Ann and Jenny to sleep on the sofa.

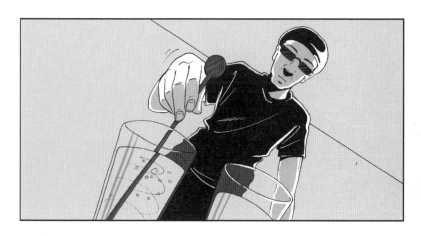

Yasmin's drink was spiked now, but she never knew it.

Name:
Luke Smith
Age:
I6

Chapter 5

Switching drinks over is not hard for a ghost. I took care to do it when no one was looking. I took care not to be seen. Soon the man in the sun glasses was fast asleep, trapped by his own trick.

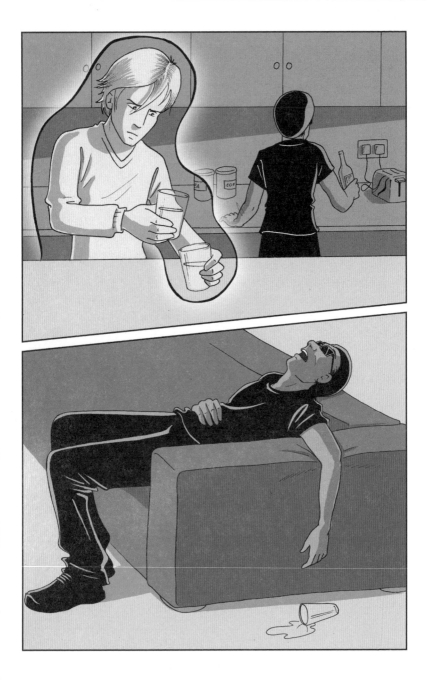

When he was asleep, Yasmin could hear a noise from below. She went down and saw a door with a key in the lock.

The five missing girls were in there.
Two of them needed a doctor badly.

Yasmin called the police on her mobile. The man in the sun glasses woke up to find himself in a police cell.

Like this book? Why not try the next one?

Fire Escape

Luke Smith is dead. But he's back to help those who need it.

Dan has been kidnapped by a gang. Can Luke help him?

For more info check out our website:
www.barringtonstoke.co.uk

Watch out for more Dead Man Files books ...

Secret Santa

There's a killer on the loose and Luke's brother's in trouble ... has Luke met his match?

The Look-out

Two men plan to rob Luke's gran and will stop at nothing to get what they want ... Can Luke save her?

For more info check out our website:
www.barringtonstoke.co.uk